THE SECRET WATER

A Chinese Folk Tale

Retold by Daphne Liu

Illustrated by
Jean and Mou-sien Tseng

HAMPTON-BROWN

Characters

Shu Fa

Uncle and Auntie

Voice of the Mountain

Shu Fa's village needs water. How can she help?

THE SECRET WATER

Shu Fa lives with Uncle and Auntie.
They live in a village by the mountain.
The land is dry and dusty. There is no
water near the village.

Every day, the villagers walk over the mountain to get water.

They fill their buckets. Then they carry
the heavy buckets home.

♪ Song

We Need Water!

I carry two buckets.
You carry one.
We need water.
We work in the sun.

I carry one bucket.
You carry two.
We cannot rest.
We have work to do!

One day, Shu Fa goes to get water.
Along the way, she finds a turnip. It is
perfect for lunch! She pulls the thick leaves.

Snap!

Water pours from the hole. Shu Fa jumps!
She thinks, "Now we do not have to walk
so far for water." She is so happy!

Suddenly, a strong wind blows. It pushes the turnip back into the hole. A loud voice says, "Do not touch my water!"

Shu Fa asks, "Who are you?"

"I am the Voice of the Mountain.

This is MY water. Tell no one about it!"

"But we need water!" Shu Fa cries.

"No! I do not share!" the Voice says.

Shu Fa runs home from the mountain.
She wants to tell about the secret water,
but she is afraid.

Many days pass. Shu Fa watches the villagers. They work so hard to get water! Shu Fa worries about the village. She worries about Auntie and Uncle. Shu Fa's long, black hair turns white.

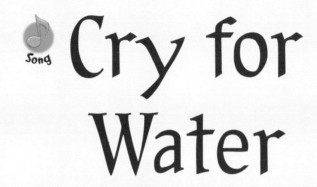

Cry for Water

Poor old Auntie!
She works under the sun.
She cries for water, and
She's not the only one.

Poor old Uncle!
He works under the sun.
He cries for water, and
He's not the only one.

One day, Uncle trips and hurts his head.
"*Aiya!*" he cries.
 Shu Fa cries, too. She must help her uncle.
She must bring water closer to the village!

Shu Fa runs up the mountain. She smashes the turnip. Water pours out of the hole.

The water flows and flows. It becomes a river. The villagers see the water. They are so happy!

The River

Now there is a river.
It is big! It is near!
The people can get water.
They shout, and they cheer.

Now there is a river.
It is wide! It is long!
The people are not crying.
They are happy and strong.

Shu Fa watches the happy villagers. Suddenly, the Voice of the Mountain shouts, "Shu Fa, you told my secret! Now you must live in my river forever."

Shu Fa cries, "Please let me say good-bye to my family!"

The Voice grumbles, "Go. But be back here tonight."

Shu Fa runs down the mountain.
"What can I do?" she thinks. "I do
not want to live in the river!"

Shu Fa finds Uncle. She tells him the problem.

"I have a plan," Uncle says.

Uncle works all day. He carves a statue out of stone.

That night, Shu Fa goes to the mountain.
Uncle is there.

"This statue will trick the Voice of the
Mountain," he says. "I just need your hair."

Uncle cuts Shu Fa's long, white hair. He
puts it on the statue.

Uncle puts the statue in the river.
Water flows over the statue. The white
hair forms a waterfall.

The Voice of the Mountain says to
the statue, "Hello, Shu Fa!"

The trick worked!

Today, the waterfall still flows to the village.
The land is green. The people are happy.
And Shu Fa has long, black hair again.